Verbal Reasoning:

Cloze Tests

Mixed Format

Book 3

How to use this book to make the most of 11 plus exam preparation

It is important to remember that for 11 plus exams there is no national syllabus, no pass mark and no retake option. It is therefore vital that your child is fully primed to perform to the best of their ability so that they give themselves the best possible chance on the day.

Unlike similar publications, the **First Past The Post®** series uniquely assesses your child's performance on a question-by-question basis, helping to identify areas for improvement and providing suggestions for further targeted tests. By entering the unique Peer-Compare™ access code for this book on our website, your child's performance can be compared anonymously to that of others who have taken the same tests.

Verbal Reasoning: Cloze Tests

Cloze tests are passages with missing words or letters which require the child to recognise and select the answer from a set of several options, or to complete the word with the correct spelling. They are designed to test a child's vocabulary and spelling.

This book covers the three main question styles of cloze tests: Word Bank, Multiple Choice and Partial Words.

Never has it been more useful to learn from mistakes!

Students can improve by as much as 15%, not only by focused practice, but also by targeting any weak areas.

How to manage your child's practice

To get the most up-to-date information, visit our website, www.elevenplusexams.co.uk, the UK's largest online resource for 11 plus, with over 65,000 webpages and a forum administered by a select group of experienced moderators.

About the authors

The Eleven Plus Exams' **First Past The Post®** series has been created by a team of experienced tutors and authors from leading British universities.

Published by Technical One Ltd t/a Eleven Plus Exams

With special thanks to the children who tested our material at the ElevenPlusExams centre in Harrow.

ISBN: 978-1-912364-78-7

Copyright © ElevenPlusExams.co.uk 2018

Second edition

elevenplusexams
head for success

About Us

At Eleven Plus Exams, we supply high-quality 11 plus tuition for your children. Our free website at **www.elevenplusexams.co.uk** is the largest website in the UK that specifically prepares children for the 11 plus exams. We also provide online services to schools and our **First Past The Post®** range of books has been well-received by schools, tuition centres and parents.

Eleven Plus Exams is recognised as a trusted and authoritative source. We have been quoted in numerous national newspapers, including *The Telegraph*, *The Observer*, the *Daily Mail* and *The Sunday Telegraph*, as well as on national television (BBC1 and Channel 4), and BBC radio.

Our website offers a vast amount of information and advice on the 11 plus, including a moderated online forum, books, downloadable material and online services to enhance your child's chances of success. Set up in 2004, the website grew from an initial 20 webpages to more than 65,000 today, and has been visited by millions of parents. It is moderated by experts in the field, who provide support for parents both before and after the exams.

Don't forget to visit **www.elevenplusexams.co.uk** and see why we are the market's leading one-stop shop for all your 11 plus needs. You will find:

- ✓ Comprehensive quality content and advice written by 11 plus experts
- ✓ Eleven Plus Exams online shop supplying a wide range of practice books, e-papers, software and apps
- ✓ Lots of FREE practice papers to download
- ✓ Professional tuition service
- ✓ Short revision courses
- ✓ Year-long 11 plus courses
- ✓ Mock exams tailored to reflect those of the main examining bodies

Other Titles in the First Past The Post® Series
11+ Essentials Range of Books

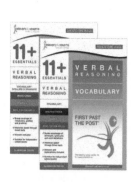

978-1-912364-60-2	Verbal Reasoning: Cloze Tests Book 1 - Mixed Format
978-1-912364-61-9	Verbal Reasoning: Cloze Tests Book 2 - Mixed Format
978-1-912364-78-7	Verbal Reasoning: Cloze Tests Book 3 - Mixed Format
978-1-912364-79-4	Verbal Reasoning: Cloze Tests Book 4 - Mixed Format
978-1-912364-62-6	Verbal Reasoning: Vocabulary Book 1 - Multiple Choice
978-1-912364-63-3	Verbal Reasoning: Vocabulary Book 2 - Multiple Choice
978-1-912364-64-0	Verbal Reasoning: Vocabulary Book 3 - Multiple Choice
978-1-912364-65-7	Verbal Reasoning: Vocabulary, Spelling and Grammar Book 1 - Multiple Choice
978-1-912364-66-4	Verbal Reasoning: Vocabulary, Spelling and Grammar Book 2 - Multiple Choice
978-1-912364-68-8	Verbal Reasoning: Vocabulary in Context Level 1
978-1-912364-69-5	Verbal Reasoning: Vocabulary in Context Level 2
978-1-912364-70-1	Verbal Reasoning: Vocabulary in Context Level 3
978-1-912364-71-8	Verbal Reasoning: Vocabulary in Context Level 4
978-1-912364-74-9	Verbal Reasoning: Vocabulary Puzzles Book 1
978-1-912364-75-6	Verbal Reasoning: Vocabulary Puzzles Book 2
978-1-912364-76-3	Verbal Reasoning: Practice Papers Book 1 - Multiple Choice
978-1-912364-77-0	Verbal Reasoning: Practice Papers Book 2 - Multiple Choice

978-1-912364-02-2	English: Comprehensions Classic Literature Book 1 - Multiple Choice
978-1-912364-03-9	English: Comprehensions Classic Literature Book 2 - Multiple Choice
978-1-912364-05-3	English: Comprehensions Contemporary Literature Book 1 - Multiple Choice
978-1-912364-06-0	English: Comprehensions Contemporary Literature Book 2 - Multiple Choice
978-1-912364-08-4	English: Comprehensions Non-Fiction Book 1 - Multiple Choice
978-1-912364-09-1	English: Comprehensions Non-Fiction Book 2 - Multiple Choice
978-1-912364-23-7	English: Comprehensions Poetry Book 1 - Multiple Choice
978-1-912364-14-5	English: Mini Comprehensions - Inference Book 1
978-1-912364-15-2	English: Mini Comprehensions - Inference Book 2
978-1-912364-16-9	English: Mini Comprehensions - Inference Book 3
978-1-912364-11-4	English: Mini Comprehensions - Fact-Finding Book 1
978-1-912364-12-1	English: Mini Comprehensions - Fact-Finding Book 2
978-1-912364-21-3	English: Spelling, Punctuation and Grammar Book 1
978-1-912364-22-0	English: Spelling, Punctuation and Grammar Book 2
978-1-912364-00-8	English: Practice Papers Book 1 - Multiple Choice
978-1-912364-01-5	English: Practice Papers Book 2 - Multiple Choice
978-1-912364-17-6	Creative Writing Examples 1
978-1-912364-24-4	Creative Writing Examples 2

978-1-912364-30-5	Numerical Reasoning: Quick-Fire Book 1
978-1-912364-31-2	Numerical Reasoning: Quick-Fire Book 2
978-1-912364-32-9	Numerical Reasoning: Quick-Fire Book 1 - Multiple Choice
978-1-912364-33-6	Numerical Reasoning: Quick-Fire Book 2 - Multiple Choice
978-1-912364-34-3	Numerical Reasoning: Multi-Part Book 1
978-1-912364-35-0	Numerical Reasoning: Multi-Part Book 2
978-1-912364-36-7	Numerical Reasoning: Multi-Part Book 1 - Multiple Choice
978-1-912364-37-4	Numerical Reasoning: Multi-Part Book 2 - Multiple Choice

978-1-912364-43-5	Mathematics: Mental Arithmetic Book 1
978-1-912364-44-2	Mathematics: Mental Arithmetic Book 2
978-1-912364-45-9	Mathematics: Worded Problems Book 1
978-1-912364-46-6	Mathematics: Worded Problems Book 2
978-1-912364-52-7	Mathematics: Worded Problems Book 3
978-1-912364-47-3	Mathematics: Dictionary Plus
978-1-912364-50-3	Mathematics: Crossword Puzzles Book 1
978-1-912364-51-0	Mathematics: Crossword Puzzles Book 2
978-1-912364-48-0	Mathematics: Practice Papers Book 1 - Multiple Choice
978-1-912364-49-7	Mathematics: Practice Papers Book 2 - Multiple Choice

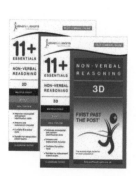

978-1-912364-87-9	Non-Verbal Reasoning: 2D Book 1 - Multiple Choice
978-1-912364-88-6	Non-Verbal Reasoning: 2D Book 2 - Multiple Choice
978-1-912364-85-5	Non-Verbal Reasoning: 3D Book 1 - Multiple Choice
978-1-912364-86-2	Non-Verbal Reasoning: 3D Book 2 - Multiple Choice
978-1-912364-83-1	Non-Verbal Reasoning: Practice Papers Book 1 - Multiple Choice

Contents

BLANK PAGE

FIRST PAST THE POST®

Word Bank

Test 1

Total /24

  12 minutes

Word Bank

designated	diversity	vast	movement	pilgrimage	local
protection	involved	annual	phenomenal	inhabit	recognition

The Serengeti National Park

Situated in northern Tanzania in East Africa, the Serengeti National Park is a (1)_____

savannah ecosystem. It is (2)_____ as a UNESCO World Heritage Site and is entitled to

special (3)_____ for its wildlife. The name 'Serengeti' originates from that given to the area

by the (4)_____ Maasai people, 'siringet'. This translates as 'place where the land extends

forever'.

Thousands of species (5)_____ the Serengeti, including wildebeests, gazelles, zebras,

elephants, lions, leopards, cheetahs and a large (6)_____ of birds. The Serengeti is most

renowned for its (7)_____ migration of wildebeests in a clockwise (8)_____

around the park and into the nearby Maasai Mara National Reserve in Kenya, which borders the

Serengeti to the north. In addition to the more than a million wildebeests which take part, 200,000

zebras and 500,000 gazelles are also (9)_____, making it a truly (10)_____

event. It has achieved global (11)_____, becoming something of a place of

(12)_____ for wildlife photographers, cameramen and cinematographers.

Test 1 (continued)

Word Bank					
territory	politicians	riots	assassinate	creation	over
betrayed	author	emperor	sparked	playwright	centuries

Julius Caesar

Julius Caesar is one of the most famous Roman **(13)**_____, known for extending Rome's

control of Europe, expanding their **(14)**_____ into modern-day France and Belgium, and

invading Britain for the first time. He was born in Rome in the year 100 BCE and lived for 55 years.

During his lifetime, Caesar was an **(15)**_____, an army general and, eventually, a dictator.

He had three children: Julia and Caesarion, and Augustus, whom he adopted. Augustus grew up to

become the first official **(16)**_____ of the Roman Empire, and ruled for

(17)_____ 40 years.

Despite Caesar's powerful position, he was **(18)**_____ by senators who conspired to

(19)_____ him in 44 BCE. His death **(20)**_____ a series of

(21)_____ across Rome, which resulted in the fall of the Roman Republic and the

(22)_____ of the Roman Empire. The renowned **(23)**_____ William

Shakespeare wrote a play based on Caesar in 1599, over 16 **(24)**_____ after Caesar's

death.

Test 2

Word Bank					
position	touching	relatives	flat	adults	palm
commonly	expressions	completely	communication	primary	communicating

Sign Language

Sign language is the use of hand movements and facial **(1)**_____ to communicate. There

are 70 million people around the world who use sign language as their **(2)**_____ method of

(3)_____, although each country has its own variation. The language is most

(4)_____ used by deaf children and deaf **(5)**_____, but also by those who for

various reasons are unable to speak, and by their friends and **(6)**_____.

When **(7)**_____, a subtle difference in the **(8)**_____ or tilt of the hand can

(9)_____ change the meaning of a word. For example, in American Sign Language (ASL),

the only difference between 'good' and 'bad' is the orientation of the **(10)**_____.

Moreover, many signs have the same meaning. For example, in British Sign Language (BSL), you start

with a **(11)**_____ hand **(12)**_____ your chin and move it away to say both

'please' and 'thank you'.

Word Bank					
devoted	community	campaigned	capable	acclaimed	victim
rose	illustrates	legacy	adversity	overcome	resolve

Maya Angelou

Maya Angelou was an (13)_____ American poet and civil rights activist who

(14)_____ much of her life to fighting for the rights of the African-American

(15)_____ in the USA. She (16)_____ alongside the famous activists Martin

Luther King Jr. and Malcolm X. Angelou (17)_____ to international fame after publishing

her first autobiography, *I Know Why the Caged Bird Sings*, in 1969. The book (18)_____ the

prejudice and (19)_____ which Angelou, like many other African Americans, was a

(20)_____ of from a young age.

Despite the hardships she faced, Angelou demonstrated strong (21)_____, allowing her to

(22)_____ her problems and develop into a strong, (23)_____ woman who

fought for justice for herself and others. Angelou passed away in 2014, but her

(24)_____, as an inspiration to those who still face racism today, lives on.

Test 3

Total

/24

 12 minutes

Word Bank					
thinking	exceptionally	afford	musicians	wealthy	period
classical	signifies	science	experience	flourished	bridging

The Renaissance

The Renaissance is the name given to the **(1)**_____ of time between the fourteenth and

seventeenth centuries in Europe. It was a time when **(2)**_____, art, literature and music

(3)_____ and developed, **(4)**_____ the gap between the Middle Ages and

modern history. Italy was at the heart of the Renaissance, with key thinkers, painters, writers and

(5)_____ residing in Rome, Venice and Florence. The word 'renaissance' translates from

French as 'rebirth', which **(6)**_____ the rediscovery of **(7)**_____ subjects,

values and ways of **(8)**_____.

One of the most famous thinkers associated with the Renaissance was Leonardo da Vinci. He was an

(9)_____ talented painter, sculptor, architect, engineer and writer, amongst other things.

As an affluent member of society, Leonardo could **(10)**_____ to spend money on art,

theatre and his other hobbies. However, the majority of Europe's population was not

(11)_____ enough for this, so they did not **(12)**_____ the Renaissance in the

same way.

Word Bank					
survived	prowess	perfectly	mystery	invasion	ruins
above	purpose	carried	believe	wiped	technology

Machu Picchu

Machu Picchu, the (13)_____ of an Incan citadel, lies 2,430 metres (14)_____

sea level, high up in the Andean Mountains of Peru. The city (15)_____ the

sixteenth-century Spanish (16)_____ of South America, which (17)_____ out

many Incan structures. The site is an example of the architectural (18)_____ of Incan

civilisation, as its stones were (19)_____ cut to fit together without the need for mortar.

Remarkably, each stone was (20)_____ by hand to the top of the mountain without the

use of the more advanced (21)_____ we possess today. There are many theories as to

Machu Picchu's original (22)_____. Some archaeologists suspect it was once a religious

site, whilst others (23)_____ it was the home of Incan nobility. The real reason for its

construction remains a (24)_____.

Word Bank

artist	parliament	campaigns	numerous	vote	lecturing
education	aimed	suffrage	passion	married	lecturer
statue	anniversary	warehouse	leading	admitted	political
tirelessly	rights	awarded	commemorate	designed	speech

Millicent Fawcett

Millicent Garrett Fawcett was born in 1847 in Suffolk to a **(1)**_____ owner named Newson

Garrett, and Louisa Dunnell. At the age of 19, she heard a **(2)**_____ by John Stuart Mill, a

member of **(3)**_____, on the topic of universal women's **(4)**_____, which is the

right to vote in **(5)**_____ elections. This sparked a **(6)**_____ in her and she

became heavily involved in his **(7)**_____. For the rest of her life, she campaigned

(8)_____ for women's **(9)**_____ in general. She published

(10)_____ essays and books, and co-founded Newnham College at the University of

Cambridge in 1871. The college **(11)**_____ to provide women with a university

(12)_____, despite the fact that they were not **(13)**_____ as members of the

university or **(14)**_____ degrees until 1948.

She **(15)**_____ the Liberal politician Henry Fawcett in 1967, with whom she had one child,

Philippa Fawcett. Philippa went on to become a **(16)**_____ mathematician and

(17)_____, setting up several schools in South Africa and **(18)**_____ in

mathematics at Newnham.

To **(19)**_____ the one-hundredth **(20)**_____ of women over the age of 30

being allowed to **(21)**_____ in the UK, Millicent Garrett Fawcett was the first woman to

receive a **(22)**_____ in Parliament Square. It was **(23)**_____ by the

Turner-Prize-winning **(24)**_____ Gillian Wearing. Fawcett's legacy lives on today in the

Fawcett Society, which continues her campaign for gender equality.

Test 5

 12 minutes

Word Bank					
usually	distinctive	outwards	predators	undergrowth	ranging
mechanism	nature	mammals	iconic	beast	useful
threat	gardening	years	recover	widespread	hollow
fallen	collectively	captivity	cutting	perceive	disappearing

Hedgehogs

Hedgehogs are (1)_____ found in woodland habitats, hedgerows, fields, parks and

gardens. They are (2)_____ across much of Europe and are also found in Asia, Africa and

New Zealand. There are 17 extant species of hedgehogs, (3)_____ from 400 grammes to

1.2 kilogrammes in weight. Despite their small size, an adult hedgehog travels around 1-2 kilometres

per night and has a home range of 10-20 hectares—that's a huge area for such a little

(4)_____! They live for about four to seven (5)_____ in the wild, but can live

for longer in (6)_____. Their most (7)_____ feature is their spines, which are

(8)_____ hairs made of keratin; our hair is made out of the same material. They are the

only British mammal to have them. These are most (9)_____ as a defence

(10)_____: when hedgehogs are scared or (11)_____ a threat, they roll into a

tight ball. This causes their spines to point (12)_____, providing protection from potential

(13)_____.

Although the hedgehog is one of the most recognised British (14)_____, they are rapidly

(15)_____ from our wild spaces. They are under (16)_____ from habitat loss

due to increased urban development and agricultural intensification, and their numbers have

(17)_____ by 30% over the last 10 years. Given that our gardens (18)_____

provide a habitat that is larger than all our (19)_____ reserves combined, and that this

habitat is perfect for hedgehogs, we can help them by (20)_____ in a wildlife-friendly way.

The most important things we can do are to leave out food for them, grow a wide variety of plants,

keep a compost heap and piles of leaves and (21)_____ available year-round, avoid using

slug-pellets, and create hedgehog highways across gardens by (22)_____ hedgehog-sized

holes in garden fences. With our help, hopefully hedgehog numbers will start to (23)_____

soon and we won't lose this (24)_____ animal from Britain forever.

Test 6

 12 minutes

Word Bank

horrors	glorified	battlefield	comrades	helped	harsh
diagnosed	fellow	perception	explicitly	literary	wartime
memorialised	career	hospital	capture	studied	printed
enlisted	poet	develop	style	civilians	evacuated

Wilfred Owen

Wilfred Owen is regarded by many to be Britain's greatest **(1)**_____ poet. He

(2)_____ in the army when he was just 21 years old, and went on to face the

(3)_____ of war from the front line. Early in his military **(4)**_____, he was

(5)_____ with shell shock and was **(6)**_____ from the **(7)**_____ in

order to recover. It was during his rehabilitation at a war **(8)**_____ that he met Siegfried

Sassoon, a **(9)**_____ soldier with a growing reputation as a **(10)**_____.

Sassoon **(11)**_____ Owen with his poetry, inspiring him to **(12)**_____ the

poetic **(13)**_____ we recognise today .

Owen believed that the concept of war was **(14)**_____ to encourage people to join the

army, and that **(15)**_____ in England had a warped **(16)**_____ of what war

was really like. As a result of this philosophy, much of Owen's poetry **(17)**_____ detailed the (18)_____ realities he and his (19)_____ had experienced. He wanted his

poetry to (20)_____ the futility of war.

Most of his poetry was only (21)_____ after his death, however, they have stood the test

of time and his works are still widely (22)_____ by scholars. In 1985, he was

(23)_____ in Westminster Abbey's Poets' Corner, alongside other (24)_____

greats, such as Shakespeare and Dickens.

BLANK PAGE

Multiple Choice

The Berlin Wall

The Berlin Wall was a global **(1)** ☐ symbol / ☐ picture / ☐ symbolic of the Cold War, which was a period of tense relations

between the USA and the USSR, a **(2)** ☐ fake / ☐ former / ☐ faulty name for Russia. Historians generally agree that

the war began in 1947, although there is no consensus on the exact start date. The wall was erected in

1961, forming a physical barrier between East and West Berlin. The USSR, which **(3)** ☐ bought / ☐ controlling / ☐ controlled

East Berlin, built the wall to prevent an **(4)** ☐ exodus / ☐ fleeing / ☐ entering of people into West Berlin, which was under

the collective control of the USA, the UK and France. The wall was constructed **(5)** ☐ quick, / ☐ overnight, / ☐ frequently, and,

as a result, thousands of people were left **(6)** ☐ trap / ☐ freed / ☐ stranded on one side of the **(7)** ☐ border, / ☐ hill, / ☐ stranger,

forcibly separated from their friends and family on the other. East Berliners caught trying to escape over

the wall were harshly **(8)** ☐ ignored, / ☐ punished, / ☐ disgraceful, but those who succeeded were **(9)** ☐ fled / ☐ movement / ☐ welcomed into

West Berlin. In 1989, there was merriment and **(10)** ☐ jubilation / ☐ despair / ☐ decorations as the wall was torn down and

people were free to move across Berlin. The **(11)** ☐ destroy / ☐ demolition / ☐ bricks of the wall signified the end of the

Cold War and was widely **(12)** ☐ clapped. / ☐ mourned. / ☐ celebrated.

Test 1 (continued)

Seahorses

Residing in **(13)**
☐ shallow,
☐ steep,
☐ systematic,
tropical and temperate waters around the world, seahorses are

fascinating creatures. They are comprised of a group of 54 species of fish which swim in a

(14)
☐ chaotic
☐ unique
☐ striped
upright **(15)**
☐ gait.
☐ alignment.
☐ position.
Their genus name is derived from the Greek words

'*hippos*', meaning 'horse', and '*kampos*', meaning 'sea monster', and they are named as such because of

their **(16)**
☐ character
☐ feeble
☐ characteristic
neck, which **(17)**
☐ frightens
☐ resembles
☐ resides
that of a horse.

They **(18)**
☐ are
☐ diverse
☐ range
in size from 1.5 to 35.5 centimetres in length. They feed on small crustaceans

and are highly **(19)**
☐ evolved
☐ evolution
☐ evolving
predators with a number of **(20)**
☐ adapts.
☐ adapted.
☐ adaptations.
They are able

to approach potential prey within very close range before **(21)**
☐ swimming
☐ striking
☐ flying
because they are

camouflaged, and because the shape of their head allows minimal disturbance of the surrounding

(22)
☐ water.
☐ wavy.
☐ land.
Seahorses use a special method, known as pivot feeding, for capturing their prey. This

involves rotating their snout at a high speed and **(23)**
☐ eating
☐ sucking
☐ catching
in the prey. Unusually for animals,

it is the males, not the females, which carry and **(24)**
☐ incubate
☐ cuddle
☐ scramble
the eggs.

Test 2

Total /24

 12 minutes

Cai Lun

Cai Lun was born in the year 48 CE in Guiyang, Southern China. Lun worked in the **(1)**

- [ ] courting
- [ ] court of
- [ ] tennis

the emperor of China for many years as a politician and a **(2)**

- [ ] musician
- [ ] manufacturer of musical
- [ ] reader

instruments. He is best remembered for his **(3)**

- [ ] creating
- [ ] inventor in 105 CE, when he devised a
- [ ] invention

(4)
- [ ] technique
- [ ] technical to manufacture paper. His paper-making process **(5)**
- [ ] technician

- [ ] asked
- [ ] required a variety of
- [ ] necessary

resources, including tree bark, **(6)**
- [ ] fishers
- [ ] fishing nets and silk, although his exact formula has now been
- [ ] boat

lost. To create one sheet of paper, he **(7)**
- [ ] suspended
- [ ] suspension multiple sheets of fibre in water, drained
- [ ] suspender

them and allowed them to dry.

Lun's invention was **(8)**
- [ ] dismissed
- [ ] understanding by Emperor He of Han and earned him numerous
- [ ] acknowledged

(9)
- [ ] presents:
- [ ] conversations: he was granted an aristocratic **(10)**
- [ ] accolades:

- [ ] title
- [ ] house and considerable wealth.
- [ ] public

Whilst **(11)**
- [ ] noisy
- [ ] ancient machinery has significantly sped up and improved this process, the basic
- [ ] modern

(12)
- [ ] principles,
- [ ] principals, which Lun invented, have not changed in almost 2,000 years.
- [ ] frequency,

Micronesia

The Federated States of Micronesia **(13)**
☐ comprising
☐ comprise
☐ consist
over 600 small islands, which are spread

(14)
☐ across
☐ through
☐ within
the Western Pacific Ocean, just to the north of Papua New Guinea. The islands are

(15)
☐ divided
☐ division
☐ made
into four states: Yap, Chuuk, Pohnpei and Kosrae. These are **(16)**
☐ distribution
☐ distribute
☐ distributed

over a distance of 2.6 million square kilometres, although the combined land **(17)**
☐ surface
☐ height
☐ area
of the

islands is only 702 square kilometres. The **(18)**
☐ nationality
☐ shipping
☐ national
flag is light blue with four white stars

(19)
☐ positioned
☐ setting
☐ reclining
in a diamond shape at its centre, with each star **(20)**
☐ being
☐ representative
☐ representing
one of

the four states. Although their official language is English, each state has its own **(21)**
☐ regionary
☐ regional
☐ regions

languages, which vary considerably. **(22)**
☐ Culture
☐ Cultural
☐ Cultured
traditions also differ between the states, but

common to all four is a strong sense of **(23)**
☐ belonging.
☐ belowing.
☐ bellowing.
People in Micronesia are typically part of

an extended family and **(24)**
☐ clan
☐ clade
☐ clam
system which strengthens their connection to the land.

Total

/24

 12 minutes

Camels

Commonly found in the Middle East, North Africa and Central Asia, camels **(1)** ☐ thrive / ☐ thriving / ☐ thrived in warm

climates. In fact, camels are able to **(2)** ☐ stands / ☐ withstand / ☐ understand changes in body temperature that would kill

most other animals. One of the main reasons for this is their ability to **(3)** ☐ confit / ☐ conserve / ☐ confiscate water. Camels

only lose around 1.3 litres of water per day, whilst other **(4)** ☐ stock / ☐ dairy / ☐ livestock in similar

(5) ☐ conditioning / ☐ conditions / ☐ conditioner lose around 20-40 litres per day!

Despite the common misconception, a camel's hump is a **(6)** ☐ reservoir / ☐ reservation / ☐ reverse of fat, not water, which it

uses as an energy **(7)** ☐ store / ☐ shop / ☐ storing when food is **(8)** ☐ rarity. / ☐ plentiful. / ☐ scarce. Another of their **(9)** ☐ essence / ☐ key / ☐ necessity

adaptations is the **(10)** ☐ shape / ☐ coloured / ☐ colour of their fur; this becomes lighter in the summer in order to reflect

more light and keep them **(11)** ☐ cool. / ☐ cooling. / ☐ hip. The **(12)** ☐ major / ☐ general / ☐ majority of the world's camels are

dromedary camels, which have just one hump, whilst only 6% are Bactrian camels, which have two

humps.

Helen Keller

Helen Keller was born in the late nineteenth century in Alabama, in the south of the USA. At around 19

months old, she **(13)**
- [ ] contracted
- [ ] develop
- [ ] fallen

a serious, unknown illness, which left her deaf and blind for the

rest of her life. Despite these **(14)**
- [ ] obstacle,
- [ ] disabilities,
- [ ] trouble,

she learned to understand other people's speech by

(15)
- [ ] movement
- [ ] felt
- [ ] running

her hands over their lips, as well as becoming **(16)**
- [ ] apt
- [ ] adept
- [ ] adapted

at reading

braille and signing with her hands. She **(17)**
- [ ] taught
- [ ] teach
- [ ] learned

herself to speak and went on to become a

world-famous speaker and author. She devoted much of her life to **(18)**
- [ ] spoken
- [ ] advocating
- [ ] advocated

on

(19)
- [ ] position
- [ ] duty
- [ ] behalf

of those with disabilities. In 1904, she became the first deaf-blind person to receive a

Bachelor of Arts **(20)**
- [ ] degree
- [ ] subject
- [ ] appointment

when she **(21)**
- [ ] graduated
- [ ] moved
- [ ] left

from Radcliffe College,

Harvard University.

Her remarkable achievements have **(22)**
- [ ] caused
- [ ] warranted
- [ ] led

her birthday, the 27th June, being celebrated as

'Helen Keller Day' in the USA. Her **(23)**
- [ ] admiring
- [ ] impressing
- [ ] inspiring

life is a **(24)**
- [ ] continued
- [ ] continue
- [ ] continuous

reminder to us

all that nothing should stop us from achieving our goals.

Test 4

Total

/24

 12 minutes

Crude Oil

Crude oil is a fossil **(1)** ☐ fuel / ☐ fuelled / ☐ fuelling which is used as an energy **(2)** ☐ source / ☐ sorcerer / ☐ sauce across the world. It

was formed hundreds of millions of years ago when organisms such as plankton, which are minute plants

and animals, died and **(3)** ☐ sank / ☐ sunken / ☐ sinked to the bottom of the oceans. Their **(4)** ☐ remains / ☐ remainder / ☐ reminds were

covered by layers of mud, which **(5)** ☐ creating / ☐ creatine / ☐ created high pressures and temperatures, the

(6) ☐ combination / ☐ combined / ☐ combine effects of which turned the organic **(7)** ☐ matters / ☐ matte / ☐ material into crude oil.

As a result of this formation **(8)** ☐ procession, / ☐ processor, / ☐ process, crude oil is found **(9)** ☐ before / ☐ beneath / ☐ deeper layers of mud

and rock at the bottom of the oceans and is very difficult to **(10)** ☐ excerpt. / ☐ extract. / ☐ except.

In order to reach these crude oil **(11)** ☐ reservation, / ☐ reverses, / ☐ reserves, which are usually located between 2,500 and

3,000 metres below ground, companies drill **(12)** ☐ depth / ☐ deepest / ☐ deep into the earth's surface. A few months

after the initial **(13)** ☐ drill / ☐ drilling / ☐ drilled process, a special fluid is pumped into the **(14)** ☐ lengthen / ☐ lengthy / ☐ longest hole

22

that the drill has left behind. As the fluid is **(15)**
☐ flowed
☐ pumped
☐ flooded
in at high pressure, cracks form in the

(16)
☐ surrounding
☐ superficial
☐ surrounded
rock, releasing the trapped crude oil and natural gas. This process is known as

fracking.

Crude oil and natural gas are **(17)**
☐ non-renewed
☐ non-flammable
☐ non-renewable
energy sources. This means that there are only

(18)
☐ infinite
☐ finished
☐ finite
supplies of these resources on Earth, and they are not **(19)**
☐ reaped
☐ repeated
☐ replenished
as

they are used up. Therefore, scientists are searching for **(20)**
☐ alternative
☐ objective
☐ subjective
sources of energy which

are renewable, inexpensive and not **(21)**
☐ harmful
☐ harming
☐ harmless
to the environment. Examples of renewable

energy resources include **(22)**
☐ solar
☐ sun
☐ solarise
power, wind power, nuclear power and hydroelectric

power, which is electricity **(23)**
☐ deducted
☐ derived
☐ divided
from the energy of **(24)**
☐ flowed
☐ flowing
☐ flow
water.

Total

/24

12 minutes

The Aztec Empire

The Aztec Empire **(1)**
- [ ] existed
- [ ] existence
- [ ] exists

from the early fifteenth **(2)**
- [ ] centenary
- [ ] century
- [ ] centuries

to 1521 CE, when a

combination of **(3)**
- [ ] disease
- [ ] diseased
- [ ] ill

and Spanish **(4)**
- [ ] conquested
- [ ] conquests
- [ ] conquestor

ended their rule. The empire was

made up of several **(5)**
- [ ] ethnically
- [ ] ethnic
- [ ] ethnicities

diverse peoples **(6)**
- [ ] ruled
- [ ] overseeing
- [ ] oversight

by indirect means.

At its **(7)**
- [ ] top,
- [ ] peak,
- [ ] summit,

the empire **(8)**
- [ ] expands
- [ ] extension
- [ ] extended

from the Pacific Ocean in the west to the Gulf

of Mexico in the east, and from what is now central Mexico in the north to what is now Guatemala in the

south. Had it not been for the **(9)**
- [ ] arrival
- [ ] announcement
- [ ] disappearance

of Europeans, the **(10)**
- [ ] organisation
- [ ] institution
- [ ] civilisation

might have continued to expand and **(11)**
- [ ] devolve,
- [ ] decrease,
- [ ] develop,

and may still have been here today.

As well as for their empire and its downfall, the Aztecs are well known for their unique culture. The

ancient Aztec religion was **(12)**
- [ ] polyglot,
- [ ] polytheistic,
- [ ] polygon,

meaning that it has several gods, like the ancient

Roman and Greek religions, and like Hinduism today. It seems that it was **(13)**
- [ ] characteristic
- [ ] characterful
- [ ] characterised

by an

appreciation of nature and the **(14)**
- [ ] cycle
- [ ] circling
- [ ] oval

of life. They regularly sacrificed human life in

gratitude and payment to the gods for the continuation of the seasons, harvests and days. This earned

them a **(15)**
- [ ] repugnance
- [ ] repetition
- [ ] reputation

as an uncivilised society, **(16)**
- [ ] notoriety
- [ ] notice
- [ ] notorious

for their violent

practices and **(17)**
- [ ] tendencies.
- [ ] tendons.
- [ ] attendance.

However, this belief is **(18)**
- [ ] unsolicited;
- [ ] unfounded;
- [ ] undisputed;

in fact, they

developed highly advanced **(19)**
- [ ] music
- [ ] teachers
- [ ] systems

for keeping records and for keeping time, and employed

a **(20)**
- [ ] complexities
- [ ] complicit
- [ ] complicated

hierarchical ruling system. They also **(21)**
- [ ] thought
- [ ] valued
- [ ] found

education highly and

were one of the first societies to **(22)**
- [ ] enforce
- [ ] enlist
- [ ] embellish

mandatory education for all children,

(23)
- [ ] regardless
- [ ] especially
- [ ] nevertheless

of rank or **(24)**
- [ ] gendered.
- [ ] gender.
- [ ] gendering.

Test 6

12 minutes

Pocahontas

Pocahontas, also known as Matoaka and Amonute, was a Native American who lived in what is now

Virginia in the USA, at around the **(1)**
- [ ] turn
- [ ] tern
- [ ] turned

of the seventeenth century. The name 'Pocahontas'

loosely **(2)**
- [ ] translates
- [ ] translation
- [ ] translating

into English as 'lively one' or **(3)**
- [ ] 'play
- [ ] 'life
- [ ] 'playful

one', and is thought to be

(4)
- [ ] positive
- [ ] representative
- [ ] superlative

of her **(5)**
- [ ] character.
- [ ] appearance.
- [ ] intelligence.

Her father was Powhatan, the **(6)**
- [ ] principle
- [ ] heading
- [ ] leader

of a **(7)**
- [ ] network
- [ ] mesh
- [ ] net

of Native American tribes, who led a **(8)**
- [ ] revision
- [ ] relief
- [ ] rebellion

against the English.

Pocahontas was alive at the beginning of the period of English settlement of America, when hundreds of

English settlers were **(9)**
- [ ] living
- [ ] migrating
- [ ] fighting

across to North America to **(10)**
- [ ] fund
- [ ] found
- [ ] establishing

English

colonies. Pocahontas and her **(11)**
- [ ] tribal
- [ ] grouping
- [ ] tribe

had many **(12)**
- [ ] interacting
- [ ] interacts
- [ ] interactions

with the English

colonists who **(13)**
- [ ] founded
- [ ] settled
- [ ] imagined

near them. Sometimes these interactions were **(14)**
- [ ] piecing
- [ ] piecemeal
- [ ] peaceful

and they traded goods, but often they fought each other. Pocahontas was **(15)**
- [ ] knowledgeable
- [ ] reknown
- [ ] renowned

for

26

her peaceful nature. According to a famous **(16)**

- [ ] anecdotal,
- [ ] anecdote,
- [ ] anaesthetic,

she **(17)**

- [ ] prevented
- [ ] allowed
- [ ] encouraged

her

father from killing the English **(18)**

- [ ] colony
- [ ] colonist
- [ ] colonise

John Smith by **(19)**

- [ ] placing
- [ ] placed
- [ ] placement

herself between

him and her father as Smith was about to be **(20)**

- [ ] executed.
- [ ] exulted.
- [ ] exuded.

However, it is uncertain how much

(21)

- [ ] telling
- [ ] truth
- [ ] truthful

there is to this story.

In 1614, Pocahontas married the Englishman John Rolfe, who had **(22)**

- [ ] established
- [ ] broken
- [ ] finished

a tobacco

plantation in Virginia. They lived at the plantation for two years, during which time Pocahontas bore their

son, Thomas Rolfe. Their marriage led to a period of peaceful **(23)**

- [ ] relatives
- [ ] relations
- [ ] relationship

between the

English settlers and the Native Americans, which lasted for eight years. The couple **(24)**

- [ ] relieved
- [ ] removed
- [ ] relocated

to England in 1616, where Pocahontas later died of unknown causes at around the age of 21.

BLANK PAGE

Partial Words

Test 1

Muhammad Ali

Muhammad Ali was an American **(1)** pr☐fes☐io☐al boxer who **(2)** c☐☐pet☐d

between 1960 and 1981. Ali participated in the heavyweight **(3)** c☐te☐☐ry and, at the young

age of 22, became the heavyweight **(4)** cha☐☐☐on in 1964, defeating Sonny Liston and

causing a major upset. By the end of his **(5)** il☐us☐☐io☐s career, he had won 56 out of 61

fights, **(6)** l☐☐ing for the first time in an official fight to Joe Frazier in 1971. His most famous

quotation is 'Float like a butterfly, **(7)** s☐i☐g like a bee', describing his own **(8)** ☐gil☐ty and

pace, which

he often used to his advantage.

Throughout his lifetime, Ali was an **(9)** a☐d☐nt activist for civil rights and racial

(10) ☐qua☐i☐y. After his **(11)** r☐t☐re☐ent from boxing, he publicly supported

many

charities and was awarded the Presidential Medal of Freedom in 2005 by President George W. Bush.

This is **(12)** re☐ar☐ed as the highest civilian award available in the USA. Unfortunately, in his later

years, Ali suffered from Parkinson's disease and passed away in 2016, aged 74.

Igloos

Igloos are dome-shaped **(13)** st ☐ ☐ ctu ☐ es built from blocks of snow. They are typically found in

the Arctic, where they are the lodgings of the Inuit and Yupik peoples. Snow provides good

(14) i ☐ su ☐ a ☐ ion because it contains trapped pockets of air, **(15)** pr ☐ te ☐ t ☐ ng

those inside from the harsh **(16)** t ☐ mp ☐ ratu ☐ es, winds and snow storms, which are

(17) typ ☐ c ☐ ☐ in the Arctic.

The inside of an igloo can be as much as 61°C warmer than the outside, when warmed by body heat

(18) a ☐ ☐ ne. The air inside **(19)** c ☐ rc ☐ l ☐ tes within the igloo, forming a convection

(20) curr ☐ n ☐ and **(21)** m ☐ i ☐ t ☐ i ☐ ing the warmth. A short tunnel is often

(22) c ☐ ☐ str ☐ cted at the entrance, which acts to **(23)** re ☐ u ☐ e heat loss and wind. A

(24) r ☐ i ☐ ed area is built inside on which people sleep. Since warm air rises, this area holds most

of the heat inside the igloo.

Test 2

 12 minutes

The Black Sea

The Black Sea is an **(1)** i ☐ la ☐ d, or a landlocked, sea located to the north of Turkey and to the

south of the Ukraine. In **(2)** a ☐ di ☐ ion to these two countries, it is **(3)** s ☐ r ☐ ou ☐ d ☐ d

by Russia, Georgia, Bulgaria and Romania. Since it is not **(4)** co ☐ ne ☐ t ☐ d to any of the world's

oceans, its tides are very **(5)** s ☐ ig ☐ t and its waters remain relatively **(6)** tr ☐ nq ☐ il.

Its name **(7)** o ☐ i ☐ i ☐ ates from an ancient system in which colours were used to

(8) re ☐ re ☐ e ☐ t the four **(9)** c ☐ rd ☐ nal points: red for south, white for **(10)**

w ☐ ☐ t,

green or light blue for east, and black for north. It is therefore thought that the Black Sea was

(11) n ☐ m ☐ d by the Achaemenids, a people who ruled over a vast **(12)** e ☐ pir ☐ from 330

to

530 BCE, and who lived just to the south of the Black Sea.

Karate

Karate, meaning 'empty hand', is a **(13)** f ☐ ☐ m of martial arts which began on Okinawa, a

Japanese island, and spread onto mainland Japan in the early twentieth century. Karate

(14) h ☐ n ☐ s important skills, including agility and **(15)** co ☐ ce ☐ tr ☐ tion. The

(16) p ☐ in ☐ ip ☐ l focus of karate is self-defence, teaching the **(17)** ph ☐ l ☐ s ☐ phy of

counter-striking your opponent rather than attacking them. A *karateka*, someone who

(18) p ☐ a ☐ ti ☐ es karate, is taught to stay calm and **(19)** co ☐ po ☐ ed when facing their

opposition, which is also a useful skill in everyday life.

Karate entered into popular fiction in the West by the 1950s and grew in popularity over the next

few decades. By the 1970s, martial arts had become its own **(20)** g ☐ n ☐ e of film,

(21) c ☐ lmi ☐ at ☐ ng in the release of *The Karate Kid*, which was **(22)** no ☐ i ☐ a ☐ ed

for both an Academy Award and a Golden Globe award. Karate now has global **(23)**

in ☐ lu ☐ n ☐ e in both popular culture and sports, and, in 2020, it will **(24)** f ☐ at ☐ re for the

first time as an event in the Summer Olympics.

The Golden Temple

Sri Harmandir Sahib, **(1)** c ☐ llo ☐ uia ☐ ly known as the Golden Temple, is an important site of

pilgrimage for Sikhs around the world and is **(2)** c ☐ ns ☐ d ☐ red to be the **(3)** h ☐ lie ☐ t

gurdwara, the name for a place of worship for Sikhs. The Gurdwara is situated in the Indian state of

Punjab, where Sikhism is the most common **(4)** re ☐ ☐ g ☐ on. It is surrounded by water, which

reflects its golden walls in the **(5)** s ☐ nl ☐ ght and creates a peaceful **(6)** at ☐ osp ☐ ☐ re.

An important tradition in Sikhism is to **(7)** of ☐ ☐ r free food, which is cooked in a community

kitchen, the langar, to anyone who enters the temple, regardless of wealth, religion, gender or

ethnicity. The Golden Temple **(8)** pr ☐ v ☐ des this charity to 35,000 people every day, and it is all

prepared and distributed by **(9)** vo ☐ ☐ nt ☐ ers.

To enter the temple's complex, both men and women have to **(10)** c ☐ ☐ er their heads and

shoulders as a sign of respect. The temple is **(11)** ap ☐ r ☐ ach ☐ ble from all four sides to show

its openness and **(12)** acc ☐ pt ☐ nce of people from all over the world.

Test 3 (continued)

Ludwig van Beethoven

Ludwig van Beethoven was a German **(13)** pi☐☐is☐ and composer. From a very young age, his

musical ability and potential was **(14)** ev☐d☐nt. This was particularly recognised by his father,

Johann van Beethoven, who was also a musician and acted as Beethoven's first music teacher. He

was **(15)** de☐cr☐b☐d as 'a young Mozart' by his friends and family from the age of thirteen,

when he **(16)** p☐bl☐sh☐d his first **(17)** col☐e☐tion of music in the form of three

piano

sonatas.

During his twenties, Beethoven's hearing began to **(18)** d☐te☐ior☐te, a problem which

continued to trouble him until his death at the age of 56. Despite this **(19)** o☐sta☐le, he

continued to compose and perform music. One of his most famous **(20)** p☐☐ces is commonly

known as 'Für Elise', which translates into English as 'For Elise'; **(21)** m☐st☐riou☐ly, the

(22) id☐☐t☐ty of 'Elise' is still **(23)** u☐ce☐☐ain. The score was

printed **(24)** p☐sth☐m☐usly in 1867, forty years after his death.

Test 4

Total

/24

 12 minutes

Eagles

Eagles have been widely used as a symbol of bravery, **(1)** m ☐ j ☐ sty and freedom across a variety

of cultures. **(2)** Ar ☐ u ☐ bly the most famous symbolic use of an eagle is that of the bald eagle as

the national bird of the United States of America. It can be found **(3)** dep ☐ c ☐ ed on various official

(4) s ☐ ☐ ls and logos across the country. Aside from being associated with admirable qualities, the

bald eagle was partly chosen as an **(5)** e ☐ bl ☐ m of the United States because it is **(6)**

n ☐ ti ☐ e

to North America.

However, this is not a necessary **(7)** c ☐ it ☐ ri ☐ n for all countries when choosing their national

animals. For example, the national animal of England is the lion, **(8)** de ☐ pi ☐ e the fact that lions

have not been found in Britain **(9)** si ☐ ☐ e before the last ice age. Even more

(10) i ☐ cong ☐ ☐ ous is the choice of the unicorn as the national animal of Scotland!

The bald eagle is not lacking in head **(11)** fe ☐ t ☐ ☐ rs as its name might suggest. It is instead

named for an older **(12)** de ☐ in ☐ ti ☐ n of the world 'bald', white patch. Therefore, its name is in

(13) re ☐ er ☐ n ☐ e to its (14) stri ☐ in ☐ ☐ y white head, which provides a

(15) be ☐ ☐ ti ☐ ul contrast with its (16) bo ☐ ☐ yellow talons and beak, and its dark

brown

body.

The bald eagle is (17) cla ☐ sif ☐ ed as a sea eagle, which means its (18) d ☐ ☐ t consists

mainly

of fish. However, like most other eagles, it eats a variety of other birds, mammals and

(19) re ☐ ti ☐ es, depending on what is (20) av ☐ il ☐ ble. Larger eagle (21) spe ☐ ie ☐ ,

such as the forest-dwelling harpy eagles, regularly (22) pr ☐ ☐ on creatures as large as monkeys

and sloths. (23) P ☐ r ☐ aps the bald eagle would be less (24) ap ☐ e ☐ ling as a national

animal

were it to do the same!

Mummification

A mummy is a human or animal body that has been **(1)** pr ☐ s ☐ rv ☐ d, either intentionally or by

(2) ac ☐ id ☐ nt through natural processes. Mummies have been found on every continent, and

(3) d ☐ li ☐ er ☐ te mummification was a feature of **(4)** s ☐ ver ☐ l ancient cultures,

(5) pa ☐ t ☐ cula ☐ ly those in very dry climates in Asia and the Americas. However, the practice

is most commonly **(6)** a ☐ soc ☐ at ☐ d with the Ancient Egyptians from around 2,800 BCE, who

embalmed their dead so that they could make the journey to the **(7)** a ☐ t ☐ rl ☐ fe.

In Ancient Egyptian **(8)** m ☐ thol ☐ gy, Anubis was the god of mummification, usually depicted with

the **(9)** b ☐ d ☐ of a human and the head of a **(10)** ja ☐ kal. He had a number of different roles,

including **(11)** pr ☐ te ☐ t ☐ r of graves, embalmer and lord of the underworld, and he also

(12) ov ☐ rs ☐ w the weighing the hearts of the **(13)** de ☐ ea ☐ ed. This process was used to

(14) d ☐ te ☐ mi ☐ e whether a soul would be allowed to enter the underworld.

Mummification was linked with **(15)** s ☐ ci ☐ l status and it was the pharaohs who were embalmed

in the most **(16)** e ☐ ab ☐ rat ☐ manner. The process would take place in a tent known as the 'ibu', where the corpse would first be washed and **(17)** p ☐ rif ☐ ed. After this, the internal organs

would be removed and **(18)** pl ☐ ☐ ed in jars, with the **(19)** e ☐ ce ☐ tion of the heart, which

was left in place as it was considered **(20)** nec ☐ ☐ sary in the underworld. **(21)** F ☐ na ☐ ly,

the body was wrapped in linen, a mask was **(22)** fit ☐ ☐ d over the face, and the body was dried out

to **(23)** pr ☐ ☐ ent decay. Mummies were then **(24)** ☐ uri ☐ d with their belongings; for

pharaohs,

this was often gold, art and other treasures.

Total

/24

 12 minutes

Jane Goodall

Jane Goodall, born in 1934, is world-famous for her **(1)** ob ☐ ☐ rv ☐ tions of wild chimpanzees

and advocation for their protection and improved **(2)** w ☐ lfa ☐ e. She **(3)** co ☐ duc ☐ ed the

first long-term study of chimpanzee behaviour, which has been **(4)** o ☐ goi ☐ g since 1960 in the

Gombe Stream National Park in Tanzania. Her **(5)** ☐ nit ☐ al discoveries were ground-breaking in

the   **(6)** s ☐ ie ☐ tif ☐ c community because they **(7)** ☐ onf ☐ ict ☐ d with two long

-held beliefs — that only humans were **(8)** a ☐ ☐ e to make and use tools, and that chimpanzees

were vegetarians. Famously, she discovered that chimpanzees hunt cooperatively and eat and **(9)**

sha ☐ e meat, and that they manufacture tools out of moss, leaves and sticks to do a **(10)**

v ☐ rie ☐ y of things. This includes fishing for termites, drinking water, and extracting various

foodstuffs — honey, birds' **(11)** eg ☐ s, and small mammals from tree trunks.

Her work in Gombe was initially **(12)** f ☐ nd ☐ d by the National Geographic Society, who also

(13) pu ☐ lici ☐ ed her work through their magazines and films. Goodall **(14)**

c ☐ pit ☐ l ☐ sed on this to raise **(15)** a ☐ ar ☐ ness of the **(16)** ☐ lig ☐ t of

chimpanzees. In 1977, she founded the Jane Goodall Institute, which supports chimpanzee **(17)**

co ☐ ser ☐ ati ☐ n and research across the world. In 1991, a global youth **(18)**

pro ☐ ram ☐ e called Roots & Shoots was set up by Goodall and a group of 16 teenagers who were

worried about **(19)** en ☐ ir ☐ ☐ m ☐ ntal

issues. Roots & Shoots now has groups in over 70 countries around the world and works to

(20) e ☐ uc ☐ te and inspire young people who hope to make a **(21)** dif ☐ ☐ ren ☐ e.

Goodall has been the **(22)** r ☐ cip ☐ ent of numerous awards, including the **(23)**

☐ res ☐ igi ☐ us Kyoto Prize, one of Japan's highest honours. She has also been bestowed with

various **(24)** ac ☐ ol ☐ de ☐ , including being named a UN Messenger of Peace,

and receiving a damehood in 2004.

BLANK PAGE

Answers

Verbal Reasoning:

Cloze Tests

Mixed Format

Book 3

Cloze Tests: Word Bank

Test 1, pages 2-3

The Serengeti National Park

1	vast
2	designated
3	protection
4	local
5	inhabit
6	diversity
7	annual
8	movement
9	involved
10	phenomenal
11	recognition
12	pilgrimage

Julius Caesar

13	politicians
14	territory
15	author
16	emperor
17	over
18	betrayed
19	assassinate
20	sparked
21	riots
22	creation
23	playwright
24	centuries

Test 2, pages 4-5

Sign Language

1	expressions
2	primary
3	communication
4	commonly
5	adults
6	relatives
7	communicating
8	position
9	completely
10	palm
11	flat
12	touching

Maya Angelou

13	acclaimed
14	devoted
15	community
16	campaigned
17	rose
18	illustrates
19	adversity
20	victim
21	resolve
22	overcome
23	capable
24	legacy

Test 3, pages 6-7

The Renaissance

1	period
2	science
3	flourished
4	bridging
5	musicians
6	signifies
7	classical
8	thinking
9	exceptionally
10	afford
11	wealthy
12	experience

Machu Picchu

13	ruins
14	above
15	survived
16	invasion
17	wiped
18	prowess
19	perfectly
20	carried
21	technology
22	purpose
23	believe
24	mystery